My Village in
Ghana

Also by Sonia and Tim Gidal

My Village in Austria
My Village in Brazil
My Village in Denmark
My Village in England
My Village in Finland
My Village in France
My Village in Germany
My Village in Greece
My Village in India
My Village in Ireland
My Village in Israel
My Village in Italy
My Village in Japan
My Village in Korea
My Village in Morocco
My Village in Norway
My Village in Spain
My Village in Switzerland
My Village in Yugoslavia
Follow the Reindeer
Sons of the Desert

My Village in Ghana

Sonia and Tim Gidal

Pantheon

To our friend Solomon Kobinah Mbroh,
who traveled with us to Makranso and
happily shared with us the hardships of
life in a tropical village

My Village in
Ghana

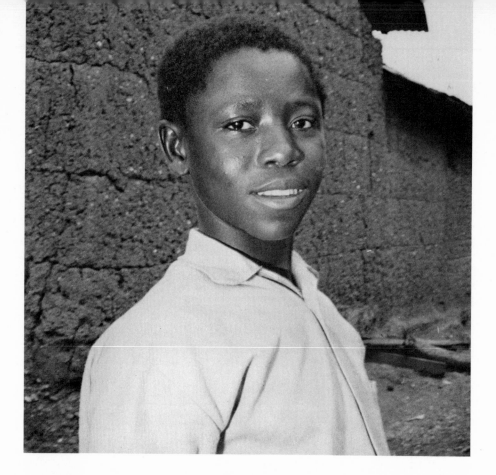

My name is James Kodjo Badu. All my relatives and friends call me Kodjo, which means "Monday" in our language. I was given this name because I was born on a Monday.

Everybody in Ghana has a middle name for the day he was born on. We have many Mondays, Tuesdays, Wednesdays, Thursdays, and Fridays in our big family.

We are usually given our first name after an honored member of the family, but sometimes it is given for a likeness to an aunt or uncle or grandfather.

I live in Ghana, which was once called the Gold Coast. People found a lot of gold here in those days, and even today we have some of the richest gold mines in the world in our country.

But more important than all the gold we have is the fact that we are the first British colony in Africa to win its independence! That was in 1957.

2

Our teacher says our nation called itself Ghana in honor of the great ancient kingdom of our ancestors. Invaders destroyed ancient Ghana over a thousand years ago.

Right now I live in Makranso village in the Ashanti region. It is about three hours by Mammy lorry from the city of Kumasi. Kumasi is the capital of Ashanti.

My mother owns one of those little buses. We call them Mammy lorries because it is usually mothers who own them. They all have names like *What's Your Mind* or *God is One* or *Never Say Die* or *Famous*. Mother named hers *Waste No Time*. She makes some money with it, and so does one of my mother's sisters.

My father is a woodcutter and driver. He drives a huge truck loaded with very long tree trunks from up north near Tamale all the way to the harbor in Accra. Last week when he passed our village he stopped awhile and we went to the lemonade shop and talked.

We are lucky that Makranso lies right on a through road, so we do not have to walk through the bush for hours to go to school or when we need a doctor.

A few months ago I decided to leave my parents and brothers and sisters and come to live with my relatives here in Makranso. I thought I might prefer the school here. We are always allowed to decide which relatives we would like to live with, and they are happy when we come to live with them. We are really all one big family.

I just walked in and said, "Here I am. I would like to stay with you awhile. I like the stories you tell in this village and I like the music you are playing on the drums. Also, I would like to live near my uncle since I will take his place some day. I will help carry water from the stream, I will help cut up vegetables, I will help with the cocoa harvest. I will also help catch the bush pig!"

I like my aunt and uncle and grandmother and great-grand-parents very much. My uncle is the chief of the village—we call him Nana, which means "chief." Nana is a very important man and hardly anything is decided without consulting him. Nana's sister is the Queen Mother of the village. All the women go to her to ask advice. Sometimes they ask about baby food and sometimes about quarrels they have had with their husbands or relatives.

It is different here than where I came from. Up north there is mostly yellow savanna land, but here there is rain forest and green

4

bush. Things grow much better here, and there are many more fruits and vegetables to eat.

I went hunting with Uncle Frederick a few nights ago. We took flashlights and rifles along and went after a bush pig. Actually it was our dog Buruburu who found the bush pig. Every day for a week I had given her a certain leaf to smell that has the same odor as the bush pig. When we started out into the bush, Buruburu immediately followed the scent of a pig. We killed two that night, which made us very happy.

Now I live in this big mud house with Nana's family. Felicia, my cousin, is calling me to help with some of her homework.

I helped rebuild the house right after the big rains. We put boards into the walls to make the mud stick again. I think we should do something about the roof too—it is made of corrugated tin, and when it rains one can not hear one's own voice—the rain sounds like a thousand fingers drumming! Perhaps we could cover it with reeds.

My aunt and grandmother and great-grandmother and great-grandfather live here too, and many of my cousins and *their* parents! It is always crowded in our courtyard—especially when Nana comes over from his own house to spend some time with his family and everyone comes to meet him. Nana's house is right across the highroad. He shares it with his sister, the Queen Mother.

5

The Nana of every village lives away from his family in his own house. His food is brought over from his family house by a son or daughter, and at night the older sons go over to sleep in his house.

Felicia says I am nicer than her brothers, because I do not tease her so much, and I help her with her homework. She also says that I can handle the long bush knife faster than her brothers when I peel vegetables. My mother taught me how to do it quickly.

Aunt Lucretia is pleased with me too. She says I am a great help to her, and I should stay with her a long time. My aunt never scolds me the way my mother does when I do things I should not do, such as catching porcupines or fooling around with crocodiles. My mother always thought I would get hurt when the porcupine started lashing its tail around with those sharp quills or if a crocodile opened its big mouth on me. But I did catch a young porcupine this year! I put it in a cage and fed it nicely and I kept it as a pet.

"Kodjo! Kodjo! You'll miss the story," calls Felicia. "Nana is just starting it. Come quickly."

"I just have to sharpen my bush knife on this stone so I can cut cassava roots while I listen," I call back.

"Kodjo, you are just like Nana," my aunt says with a laugh. "He talks with his friends while he buys cloth for me at the market! He dances and beats the drum at the same time! Nana loves to do two things at once."

Nana laughs and nods his head. "You are right. I like doing two things at the same time. Remember the time in the bush when we opened cocoa pods while we were singing? We never worked so fast! It was a good harvest that year. Let's hope we will have a good cocoa harvest again this year. Then we will have a great harvest festival—and you will get some fine new cloth, eh, Lucretia!"

"Nana, we should start picking the cocoa beans today," my aunt says happily. "I have been in the bush this morning and everything is ready: the pods are yellow, they are all ripe, and we will have a great harvest! Now let's hear your story. I will listen to you and prepare our meal. Even *I* can do two things at the same time!"

"I will tell you the story of why the snake has no legs," says Nana, as everyone gathers around.

Once upon a time all animals had legs, even the snake! They lived peacefully together working on the land: the beaver cut the trees; the elephant pulled the trunks away; the deer dug the ground; the bulls and cows plowed and fertilized it; and the porcupine made holes in it. The birds brought the seeds and dropped them into the earth. Everybody was busy. Except the snake. She always had excuses for not working.

8

One day she would say she had to take care of her great-grandmother, another that she had to write an urgent letter to the village Queen—always excuses.

When it came time for the harvest, the animals discovered that someone was stealing the juiciest vegetables from the fields. So the animals called a meeting and asked Kwaku Ananse, the clever spider, for his advice.

Kwaku Ananse said he would find the thief, "But first I must think in my hut for two nights, and while I do this you must all keep away from the fields."

"Good," thought the thief. "I shall be safe for two more nights."

The first night Kwaku Ananse did not stay in his hut but took his son to help him pour a great barrel of tar all over the finest vegetable field, making the ground all sticky. Then they climbed a tree and waited.

Soon after midnight they heard moaning and groaning: "I'm stuck in the tar! I'm stuck in the tar!" They had caught the thief!

In the morning Kwaku Ananse, who knew that the thief was still stuck in the tar, called the other animals together and told them what he had done. They all went out to the field to see who it was.

When they got there and discovered it was the snake, they were very angry. They picked up sticks to beat her. But Kwaku Ananse told them to let the snake go. This was not easy. They tied ropes around the snake and pulled and pulled and pulled, but it was no use, for the tar had hardened. Then they gave one last very hard pull and the snake stretched and stretched, and suddenly came unstuck. But to their horror the snake's legs remained stuck fast in the tar.

The animals then felt badly and took the snake home and smeared her wounds with white clay and bound them in leaves. After twelve days the wounds healed but no legs ever grew again, and to this day she remains very long and stretched.

"And now you know the reason why the snake has no legs."

"I don't like snakes!" Little Kwao says to Nana. "Please tell us another Ananse story. I like lizards, do you know one about lizards?" Kwao is the youngest of my cousins and he is very clever.

"Not now," Nana says. "I am busy now. I have to organize the cocoa harvest. What are you doing there? Are you trying to catch

9

the rooster again, Kwao? He will get angry and peck you on the legs again!"

"I want to carry him in the basket on my head," Kwao wails. "He went in before. I put three corn kernels inside. The rooster likes to eat the corn."

"Kwao," my aunt calls. "Take the basket and walk over with Nana to his house and bring me back my two dresses. Aunt Dina did laundry today. Tell her she has my blue dress with the white dots, and a white dress with black leaves and red trees painted

on it. Take Nana's hand when you cross the highroad. Since little Mary got hurt in that accident, I am so afraid. Her foot and eye still haven't healed. Mary might have been killed if that timber truck hadn't run over a goat instead of her. The goat really saved her life! Cars and buses speed on the highroad. They don't care whether they are passing a village or not!"

Nana takes Kwao's hand and together they cross the highroad to Nana's house. I go along because I want to pick up my big towel before I go to my classroom. I hope it is dry—things take a long time to dry because the air is so damp.

When we enter Nana's courtyard little Kwao says to Aunt Dina, "There are no black leaves and there are no red trees!"

"I don't know what you are talking about, Kwao," says Aunt Dina, who stands with her two children in the courtyard. "Nobody says there are black leaves and red trees in the bush."

"But I have to bring back Mama's dresses. She says you washed them today. One dress has black leaves and red trees painted on it," Kwao says. "And the other one is blue with white spots."

"You mean *dots*, Kwao! Not *spots*," says Aunt Dina. "The spots were washed out today. The dresses are right up there on the roof—do you see them? They are all dry. So that's why you were talking about black leaves and red trees!"

"Only in nature do trees have to be green," I say. Artists copy nature in different colors. They use whatever colors they like best, Kwao." Little Mensah and Manu look at me strangely.

"They don't know what you are talking about, Kodjo," Aunt Dina says. "I think Mensah wants to tell you about his bruised leg."

"The fire ate my leg, Kodjo. See, it is all red!" He wails and points at his leg. "The fire is bad! The fire doesn't like me! Mama put white powder on it, then it didn't hurt any more."

"You went too close to it, Mensah. Fire eats up everything that comes too close to it."

"It doesn't eat up your cooking pots!" Little Kwao says. Aunt Dina laughs. "You *are* clever—fire can't eat iron! But it makes it very hot, Kwao. Here are the clothes for your mama. I'll put them in the basket for you. Be careful not to drop them on the ground."

"I can even carry a rooster on my head!" Kwao says. "But he doesn't like to stay in my basket! He is silly! He wouldn't—"

"A snake! A snake! A giant snake!" somebody is shouting.

I grab a long *fufu* stick and run outside. "Stay away, children!" our policeman Asamoah shouts. "Stay away, the snake is poisonous!"

But Wabi has already killed the snake with his short stick. "Well done! Well done, Wabi!" Asamoah calls, and we all shout "Long live Wabi the snake-killer! Long live Wabi!"

"He knows exactly where to hit a snake," Asamoah says. "He should get a medal for killing snakes! It's his third one this week! And this one is a python!"

"The snake really *doesn't* have legs!" shouts little Kwabena. "Just as Nana told us in the story. He left them behind in the tar. That snake is even taller than Wabi!"

"Can I have a piece of its skin

and a tooth?" Francis asks Wabi. Francis came out too with his bush knife. "I could use the skin in school—we are just learning about different reptiles. Pythons can climb and swim and they can swallow a whole rabbit!"

"I don't like snakes at all!" Afua says, making a face. They are evil. They scare me. I saw one killing a bird down at the river!"

"Can I please have a piece of snakeskin too?" Kwao begs. "I want to make sandals from it—then the snake will have legs again. Mama got a pair of snakeskin sandals from Nana after the last cocoa harvest. But they are all ripped now." We all laugh at little Kwao's thinking he will give the snake back her legs, but Wabi says, "I will certainly give you a piece of snakeskin, Kwao, and I will show you how to make sandals from it!"

Wabi can make a lot of things. He carves spoons from calabashes and makes pots for storing palmwine. Wabi even carves little elephants from ivory and wood.

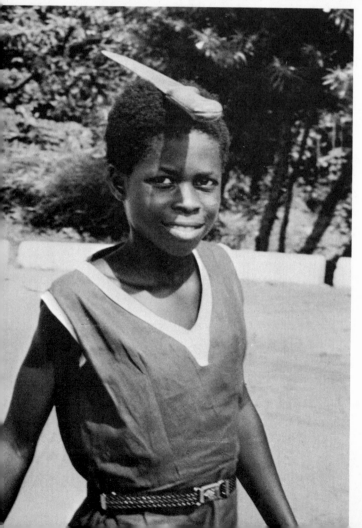

"Aren't you late for school?" I hear our teacher Opoku call when he passes us. "I am too," he says. "It's all because of that snake!"

I hurry to put the long *fufu* stick back where it belongs. Then I grab my bush knife, put some books on my head, and run up to our old school building. I am not the last one to enter the class. I pass five girls and a few boys. I pass Akua with her big bush knife. She is always the last to get to school. She has a long way to walk through the bush, so the teacher doesn't complain when she is late. Sometimes during the rainy season, she can not come to school at all because the bush road is muddy and impossible to walk on.

"Girls and boys, first let us cut the long grass in the schoolyard," Teacher Opoku tells us. "Be careful not to step on any snakes, because they will bite you if you do. Cut the grass as short as you can and put the cut grass into your pails. Later, we will feed the goats with it. After the cutting you should all come in for Bible class. We won't have any other lessons today because the chiefs are coming to the village."

We all squat down and cut the long grass. It is so hot that perspiration is running down my spine and my shirt is sticking to my body. I am glad I sharpened the blade of my knife today. It cuts very easily. Everything grows so fast that we have to cut the grass in the courtyard every few days or we couldn't play soccer. We wouldn't be able to see the ball.

We do not use a soccer ball to practice with—we use a grapefruit. We kick it until it bursts and then we take a new one to play with. Real soccer balls are too expensive for practice. Of course we use one for real school games or when we play against another school.

After we finish cutting the grass and the grounds look clean and neat, we dip our hands into a pail of cold water, wipe our faces, and walk into our classroom. It is even hotter inside because there is no ventilation. Very often we take our chairs outside and have our lesson under the beautiful shady Acacia tree, but another class is sitting there now so we have to stay inside today. We take turns having lessons under the tree.

Teacher Opoku goes to the blackboard and draws a map of ancient Israel on it—then he says, "Today we will talk about Abraham's journey. We will trace the way he went from the town of Haran to the town of Hebron.

"You will find the story of this journey in the Bible. If you were to visit Syria and Israel today, you could still walk on the same road that Abraham and his family walked on. The same roads are still there!

"Now, how long do you think it took Abraham and his family to travel from Haran to Hebron?" Teacher Opoku asks the class.

"About eight hours by Mammy lorry and five hours by car," Kofi says. "—If the road was good and it was not the rainy season!"

We all burst out laughing. "Kofi," Teacher Opoku says with a smile, "you certainly mechanized Biblical times. You should have added half an hour by jet plane! Alfred, what do you think? How long did it really take?"

"About four weeks on donkeys and one week on camels. There are many hills in the north near Haran, and the animals have to rest and be fed in between."

"That is more like it," Teacher Opoku says.

"Did Abraham leave the north because there was a great famine?" Wabi asks.

"No, Wabi. Abraham and his family went south to Canaan be-

cause the Lord appeared to Abraham and told him—"

"That he would give Abraham and his family the land," Francis shouts.

"You shouldn't interrupt, Francis," Teacher Opoku says sternly. "But you may continue."

"The Lord said to Abraham, 'get thee out of thy country, and from thy kindred and from thy father's house unto the land that I will show thee.'"

Francis is very good in Bible study, he even gets most names right and remembers who is who. I mix them all up. How can I remember names without knowing the faces?

"Right, Francis," the teacher says. "Very good. And who died in Haran? Kodjo, it's your turn to say something—you were quiet all morning. Are you thinking of a new abstract painting again? Your thoughts seem to be far away."

"Wasn't it Abraham's father?" I say meekly.

Everybody claps their hands because for once my answer is correct.

"Now, that's enough for today. Tomorrow, I want you to draw or write or tell the story of Abraham's journey. But first go over your notes from last week to refresh your memory.

"I won't give you much homework this week because of the cocoa harvest. You will all have to help. We are lucky this year—we have a rich harvest. *Tu mirika! Tu mirika!*" our teacher tells us. "Run on! Run on!" We run out of the classroom into the courtyard.

19

"I want to go to Jonathan's and pick up the new *oware* game Nana ordered," I say to my friend Francis. "Do you want to come along?"

"I have to go there anyway. My father ordered three new stools. One is for our honored guest this afternoon, when the chiefs visit our village."

"Let's play *oware* right after we pick the cocoa beans. You can eat at my house today—there will be *fufu* and pineapple, and we may even have bush meat in the bowl. Aunt Lucretia likes to put out a big spread when the Nanas come! Oh, and look for ababo seeds when you are in the bush. I lost all mine to Sowo the other day. We won't be able to play *oware* without any. I will look for some too."

"You are much too early," Jonathan says when I ask him for the *oware* game. "I had to carve many stools this week. Everybody wants everything ready before I even start. It would be better if I could work with my hands *and* my feet! I could make twice as much money!

"But I will get to your game soon, Kodjo. It still needs a good sanding. Hand it to Kwabla over there. He has just finished the three stools for your family, Francis!

"Your father ordered a circular design in redwood. So many people are ordering this moon design now. I like it very much myself. And look how beautifully the small stool for your little brother turned out, Francis!"

In our Ashanti region, the first gift a father makes to his child is a stool. I got mine a long time ago—when I started to crawl, I think. When my oldest sister was married a while ago, she got a beautiful carved stool from her husband.

"I have enough work to do today!" Kwabla says a bit angrily, when I hand him the *oware* game. "I want to be on time for Nana

Sabranu's arrival, and I have a long way home through the bush to pick up my gold helmet. I still have to sand that big carved elephant over there! The village people are presenting it to Nana Sabranu. It's mahogany—the most expensive wood there is!"

"Kwabla, do you know what Teacher Opoku told us yesterday in class? There are over a hundred different types of wood in our forests! Can you believe that? He said we export seven of these woods to other countries. They make good sturdy furniture from these trees. That's our largest export after cocoa!"

"He should know!" Kusi calls over. "After all, that's why he studied at Kumasi University!"

"Can't you carve one of those elephants yourself, Kwabla?" I ask. "Even I can carve small ones from ivory and ebony, but not a big one like that. When I squat down, it's as big as I am! I would like to learn to carve big ones. See Atakora over there—he could teach me, but he never has time for that.

"You don't have to sand the *oware* game very smooth like the stools here," I say to Kwabla. "Just give it a quick once over. Feel how wonderful the smooth wood is, though, Francis!"

"Your uncle would be angry with me if the game didn't feel smooth, Kodjo. But I will do it quickly. We have *so* much work. See the men over there sawing the white wood? Those are all orders for stools. They order them all the way from Kumasi."

"I was just in Kumasi," Francis says. "My mother's brother lives there. He is a lawyer and very rich, and he has one of those big elephants standing right next to his television set. He even has a copy of the Golden Stool standing in a special corner of the room."

"Let's go see Kusi," I say. "Maybe he has carved some new designs." Kusi is a clothprinter. He carves designs into pieces of calabash, and then he dips the carved designs into dye and stamps them on cloth.

"You know, my grandfather was in a good mood last night," Kusi says happily, when he sees us. "Usually he isn't, but yesterday he wanted to talk. I was cooking badiroots and bark in a big pot to get this black dye for printing—it takes hours and hours—and there he was. He sat down next to me and said, 'Do you know the story of our Golden Stool?' I said, 'We do not have a Golden Stool in the house.' So he said, 'I do not mean our family, I mean our old Ashanti kingdom—the stool that is with our *Asantehene,* our paramount chief, in Kumasi palace! It is hidden in a secret place known only to the *Asantehene.'*

" 'I do not know the story,' I said to Grandfather. 'I only know that the Golden Stool rests on an elephant skin and that it is very beautiful!'

" 'That is right, my boy,' he said. 'But there is much more to it! The Golden Stool has its own throne and even a bodyguard. It rests on a shield made of elephant skin, and there is a lion's skin right under it. Those two skins tell us how powerful our *Asantehene* is—as strong as the elephant and the lion together! And the stool has a goldplated drum and lute lying right next to it. I think it can hear music without anybody playing the instruments!

" 'You remember from school the legend that the old Ashanti kingdom was founded many hundreds of years ago—at the time when the Golden Stool fell from heaven, during the reign of Nana Osei Tutu.

" 'And you know that our Golden Stool is called Sikadwa Kofi— "The Golden Stool that came from heaven on a Friday." It is not just a piece of wood, my boy, it is like a living being.

" 'One of our Ashanti priests had prayed for a miracle to happen, and then the Golden Stool descended from heaven as a gift from the gods. The spot where it landed is very sacred to us. A few months ago a hospital was being built near that spot. The hospital had to be planned so that the building did not touch the sacred spot or even cast a shadow on it. I will take you to see that sacred spot one day,' Grandfather said to me. He will take me to a Durbar festival too, when the Golden Stool is carried in front of the *Asantehene* under its own big umbrella!"

"Nana told me that the Golden Stool is really the soul of our people," I say. "It unites us. And Nana told me too that there can be no

24

secrets between a man and his stool—the stool knows everything its owner knows, even after his death! He said I should never let anybody else sit on my stool. I should turn it on its side when I am not sitting on it. Otherwise someone with an evil spirit may sit on it and I may not be able to get rid of that evil spirit easily."

Where I come from, near Tamale in the north, we honor the skin more than the stool. Our Nanas sit on skins. It may be the skin of a goat or a sheep or a cow or a leopard or a lion. He may even sit on a number of skins. The fiercer the animal whose skin he sits on, the more powerful is the Nana.

"And what about doing a bit of work instead of talking so much about Golden Stools and evil spirits," says Akua, who is Kusi's

25

cousin. She is baking and selling fried "snake" cookies in the village.

"I see you are preparing my cloth. My husband is giving it to me as a present after the cocoa harvest! Kusi, don't make it less than six yards—I want to make a two-piece dress from it and use a little piece for a headdress and a little piece for the baby to be carried in. I see you invented your own *adinkra* designs again. You are a real

artist! I always leave it to you, don't I? But I am glad you put the round *adinkra* design on my cloth. To me it's the most beautiful of all designs and it will look very nice on me."

"But don't you see that Kusi put the wheel with spokes on your cloth too?" calls Angelina with little Kwami on her back. She is just walking out of the bush with a big load of firewood on her head. "As you know, it means you are a jealous person! Are you?"

"You know that for a jealous person the wheel is big and the spokes are small," Kusi calls back to Angelina. "As you see, I made the wheel small and the spokes long. That means kindness—because Akua always gives away her cookies to people who do not have enough coins to buy them!"

"Thank you very much, Kusi," Akua says happily. "I am glad you are my cousin. Next time make Angelina's cloth full of *kuntinkantan* designs—the ones that mean 'do not be arrogant!' That should teach her!" We all laugh at this, and Kusi's mother and aunt, who are standing near him, cooking and preparing more badiroots and bark for him, start giggling. Little Kwami doesn't like all the noise and he starts crying and jumping around on his mother's back. Angelina and Akua always get into quarrels over something.

I run home. I remember that I had promised my aunt I would carry water from the river.

"Kodjo!" Mary calls after me from the calabash tree. "Will you help me cut calabashes for the palmwine tomorrow? You can have the biggest one in return for your work. I have a large order for the market in Kumasi. The season for palmwine is beginning!"

"I will come over tomorrow, after I help harvest the cocoa," I call back to Mary. "My uncle will like having a new pot for his palmwine."

"You know what doctor Chofache Kwaku told me yesterday?" Mary goes on. "He said he would buy *all* my calabashes! Then he would send them to a mill in Kumasi where they squeeze the oil from them. He wants to use the oil to heal leprosy! Did you learn anything about that in school? You learn so many new things now—my daughter Dina came home and told us how men are flying to the moon! It's so hard to believe, but her teacher told her about it. No, I won't sell all my calabashes to the doctor. We need them to store palmwine and for making plates and bowls and spoons and whatnot. Always inventing those new things!

"Maybe one day none of us will have to work any more and we will all just sit around singing and telling Ananse stories. That will be the day!" Mary says and laughs.

Mary never stops talking once she has started—but everybody in the village likes her because she is kind and generous and she always takes care of people when they are sick.

I enter our courtyard and take a pail from the kitchen. Then I walk down the grassy path to the river. I take off my pants and shirt,

put them on the grass, and jump into the water. The water feels good and cool. I see a group of small children jumping up and down together in the water. Quickly I duck, swim underwater toward them, and pinch some of them on their legs. "A crocodile! A crocodile!" little Ajete shouts. "It just pinched me on the leg!" And they all start shouting and splashing out of the river. I jump up and shout out loud, "I am the crocodile! I am the crocodile!" And I duck again and swim quickly away. The whole group of them dash into the river again to try to catch me, but they don't.

It is great fun. We all know how to swim. I try to escape to the place downriver where the laundry is done. Then I get out, get my pail, and run to the place upstream where we get fresh drinking and cooking water.

The children give up the chase and the women on the riverbank shout at them not to splash so much. Their laundry on the grass is nearly dry, and it will get wet again!

Our river is divided into four parts. Upstream is the clean drinking water, then the part where we go swimming, then comes the part where we soap ourselves, and then comes the part where the laundry is washed.

29

Nobody would ever swim where we take the drinking water from and nobody would ever wash the laundry where we go swimming! There is a song we sing sometimes about our river:

River! In you we bathe
and from you we have
our drink,
From you we collect the
water to wash our
clothes.
But for you what would
we have done?
We are very grateful to
you, oh river!

"I caught a watersnake in my hand and now I lost it again!" I hear little Kwaku say to his brother Kwami when I fill my pail with drinking water.

"There are no watersnakes here!" I tell him. "It probably was a tiny earthworm!"

"No, it was a watersnake!" Kwaku insists. "Like the one Wabi killed this morning— only a little bit smaller."

"Oh, *kwasu!*" Kwami shouts. "Oh, foolish boy! You are worse than Ananse, who is always boasting! Come and help me carry the pail!"

30

"We can not carry one pail on two heads!" little Kwaku says. "I want to look for the snake. I am big and strong!"

"Ah! You sound like you should be the head of the village one day!" I say. "But then you will not only have to be big and strong but *helpful* and *nice* too. The people will not like a chief who does not help them. They will take him off his stool. They will not even listen to him!"

"I want to be chief! I will help carry the water up, Kodjo," little Kwaku says meekly. I pat him on the head. I put my pants and shirt back on, put the pail on my head, and walk with all the other children up the steep hill to our hut.

"Kodjo! Kodjo! Tell us a new Ananse story!" shouts Philip. "The mothers are cooking now! We would like to hear one, please!"

I am known in this village as a storyteller. I never told stories in my village up north, but here I like to. I'm not even sure why.

"I will!" I call. "Come to the yard! But very quietly or Great-grandmother will throw you out! You know she is very strict!"

"We will be quiet! We will be very quiet!" the boys and girls shout excitedly, jumping up and down with the waterpails shaking on their heads. The water splashes all over them, and some dash back to the river to fill them up again.

When I enter the yard Aunt Lucretia is preparing our mid-day meal and I am just in time with the fresh water.

I enter my little room, take my shirt off, take the blue and white *ntoma*, my cloth, from my bed and wrap it around my body. I always do that after school hours—it's my leisure-time cloth. But when I go to work in the bush with vegetables or cocoa, I wear my shirt, because it is easier to work with a shirt on than with a *ntoma*.

The gate to our house keeps opening and closing quietly. Kwami, Kwaku, Kofi, Kobina, Yaw, Afua, Ama, Esi, Kwao, Adjua and a few other children step into the courtyard and jump onto the veranda. Great-grandmother and Grandmother look over to them suspiciously and all of a sudden Great-grandmother nods her head. "*Akwaaba! Akwaaba!*" she says. "Welcome! Welcome!" I see Aunt Lucretia laugh to herself—she isn't used to having Great-grandmother welcome children. Aunt Lucretia loves to have many children in the yard, as long as they are quiet. She even gives them sweet-corn kernels or oranges if she has enough in the house.

"Kwaku told me he caught a snake in the water today!" Kofi shouts. "As big as the one Wabi killed this morning!"

"I know, but it swam away again!" I say. "I will tell you how Kwaku Ananse caught a snake once. Maybe Kwaku will learn from it how to catch a snake and *keep* it!"

"Please tell us the story of how the leopard got his spots," Kwami says. "You promised us last time! Please!"

"Let's hear the leopard story! Let's hear the leopard story!" Kofi shouts, but the others all hush him. They are afraid Great-grandmother will get angry and throw them out.

"All right," I say, and I start my story: "There was once a village in Ashanti that lay near a river—"

"Makranso! Makranso village!" Kofi blurts out. "*Our* village! *Our* village!"

"Hush, Kofi!" I say. "It could be any village!" I continue my story.

One day the mother of an ant died and all the animals decided to accompany the ant to the funeral.

On the way to the funeral they passed a farm full of beautiful, ripe garden-eggs. The leopard was going to the funeral too. He especially liked to eat garden-eggs. So he decided to walk more and more slowly until the funeral procession had left him far behind.

At last he was alone and he turned and rushed into the farm and sat down and ate and ate and ate the garden-eggs until he could eat no more. His belly had grown enormous! Then he slowly got up and clumsily ran to join the other animals.

At that moment the farmer came out of his house and saw that someone had stolen his lovely garden-eggs. He ran until he came to the funeral procession.

The farmer was very angry and he accused the animals of taking away his food. They all argued with him, denying that they had stolen his garden-eggs, but the farmer insisted that they should stand trial. The animals had to agree.

First the farmer made a great fire in a hollow in the ground. "Jump over it," he said to the animals. "Jump over it one by one! If you are innocent, you will not get burned by the fire, but if you are guilty you will fall into the fire and get burned, and it will serve you right!"

One by one the animals took turns jumping over the fire: some of them sang a song, some of them roared or whistled to give themselves courage before they jumped.

At last only the leopard was left, and he was so nervous that he sang and roared and whistled all at the same time. The animals were getting impatient to get to the funeral, and so they told the leopard to hurry up and jump.

The leopard took a great leap into the air, and—maybe because he was nervous knowing he was the thief, or maybe because of all those garden-eggs rumbling in his stomach—instead of jumping *over* the fire he fell right *into* it. He howled and howled and rushed from the fire as fast as he could. But it was too late—his coat was covered all over with brown and black patches. The fire had burned spots into it.

"And now you know why the leopard has spots. It doesn't pay to steal."

Everybody claps their hands after hearing my Ananse story and Grandmother says I should tell a story every day!

"Kodjo!" my aunt calls over from her cooking pots. "That was the second Ananse story today! You really can compete with Nana in storytelling." This is a great honor for me.

"The yams are cooked! Out with you children! Your mothers will

34

be looking for you!" my aunt says. The children run from the yard. "*Medase! Medase!* they yell. "Thank you! Thank you!"

We dip our hands into a pail of water and squat down in our eating corner.

"Felicia! *Bra! Bra!*" Aunt Lucretia calls. "Come here! Come here! *You* bring the food over to Nana today." And she puts a wooden box with covered dishes on her daughter's head. "And tell

Nana that he should enjoy his meal and always be happy."

The men of our family eat by themselves. The women eat together in the kitchen, and we children eat in the eating corner.

We have yams as usual and we dip them in peanut soup. We eat yams at least once a day. Then we have bananas for dessert. Everything we eat grows in the bush, except salt and bread and rice.

Aunt Lucretia makes the most delicious soups and sauces from herbs and leaves. Hers are much spicier than the ones my mother makes in my village up north. But Mother cooks many things I like too. She mashes up corn and wraps it in palmleaves. It's called *kenke* and I love to eat it.

We do not have such rich soil up in the north as we do here in Ashanti. Up there, only corn and yams and tomatoes and peppers grow—but then we can raise cattle up north and we can't do that here because there is not good grazing land.

We are much poorer where I come from: we do not have the rainfall, so we can not grow cocoa, and cocoa is what makes Ashanti rich. Because the climate up north is different, we do not have oranges and bananas and palm fruit, which one needs everyday for cooking.

35

It is quite easy to make cooking oil from the fruit of the oil palm. The men and boys climb the tall trees to cut the prickly fruit down. Then the women crack open the fruit to get the palm nuts. These are boiled for a long time and the oil just oozes out. The oil is used in soaps and cosmetics—and we dip our bread into it every day.

I went a few days ago with one of my uncles to the bush to help him get the fruit off the palm trees. Uncle Frederick said to me while we cut the palm fruit, "The oil palm is growing and gives oil although it does not have a brain!" What did he mean by that? Uncle Frederick often talks in riddles. Once when he saw me going to school with my bush knife he said to me, "The bush knife does not know its owner—that's why it cuts everybody! Be careful, Kodjo!"

"Nana says you should go to Kofi the letter-writter and have him write a letter of complaint to the government in Kumasi about the cobwebs on the telephone wires," Cousin Felicia says when she comes back from seeing Nana. "Nana said he talked about it with you yesterday."

"Yes, he did," I say. "Kofi Appiah is coming today. I looked at his table when I came back from school. His typewriter wasn't there yet."

"The Mammy lorry was late again today," Grandmother calls over. "Kofi always comes from Kumasi on *Money No Happiness*, but it broke down on the way. He should have taken *God Never Sleeps*. That one is usually on time! I didn't get the fish my daughter sent me on *Money No Happiness* in time. *Slow Old Turtle* is what that old lorry should be named, or *Fish Swim Faster*!" And she giggles.

"Listen to that child of mine complaining about slow lorries!" Great-grandmother calls to Grandmother from the corner of the yard where she sits on the steps. "I still remember when we had no cars or trucks or buses at all! We had only our feet to bring us from one place to the other—walking for hours and hours on bush trails. We got up in the middle of the night and started walking to be on time for the weekly market! *You* are lucky that our village is so close to the main road. *You* have been spoiled!"

It's little Kwao's turn to wash the dishes today after we finish

36

eating and Felicia helps him with them. Then we all brush our teeth and rinse our mouths. This morning I made new toothbrushes for all of us. I make them nearly every week.

I cut sticks from the bark of the banana tree. Then I blacken the sticks with charcoal—that keeps our teeth white. The doctors at the mobile dental clinic told us to clean our teeth after *every* meal and for a good long time.

Great-grandmother always complains that we do not wipe the black spittle off the floor quickly enough. Aunt Lucretia says that it's either healthy white teeth or black spots on the floor. We can wipe the ground, but we can not wipe off holes in our teeth! She thinks teeth are more important.

I put my sandals on, put a few coins in my pocket, and walk to Kofi Appiah. I see him sitting at his typewriter.

"I have the letter prepared in my mind already," Kofi Appiah says. "Nana was here before. The cobwebs really are heavy on the telephone wires. I saw them all along the road on my way here.

I phoned my office in Kumasi just now and I could hardly hear my boss talking!

Those spiders really disturb the sound with their webs. The telephone people must have forgotten all about it—it's been months since anybody came to clean them."

Nana is always faster than I am. Things have to be done immediately with him. "So what am I doing here when Nana already saw you?" I say to Kofi Appiah.

"Because Nana wants you to take on responsibility. Nana wants you to do things well. You will be the next Nana one day—aren't you his nephew?"

"Yes!" I say. "Nana's oldest sister is my mother. I guess I should have come to you earlier—I was being lazy. But your bus was late—and I looked for you right after school."

"Are you still painting, Kodjo?" Esi wants to know. She owns the charcoal store in the village and we always buy charcoal from her.

"Yes, I do sometimes," I say.

"Could you paint a nice big picture from the Bible for us?" Esi asks. "Abraham or Moses or something like that. We could hang it in the church! And I will give you the cardboard for it, okay?"

"You won't be able to recognize the people—I paint forms and colors only—'abstract,' you call it," I say.

"Now look," calls John from the next table where he and his brother Edward sell all kinds of merchandise. "Now look at this sandal here, Esi. If Kodjo were to paint this sandal, it wouldn't look like a sandal at all—he just puts his feelings about the sandal on the board in colors. It wouldn't even have the same shape. This he calls abstract painting."

"Don't talk such nonsense," Esi calls back, "or I will call Doctor Chofache Kwaku to give you medicine to put your brain right again —a sandal is a sandal! And that's that!"

We all start laughing, and I walk over to John and buy a red ball-point pen from him. It will be fun to write with a red ball-point for

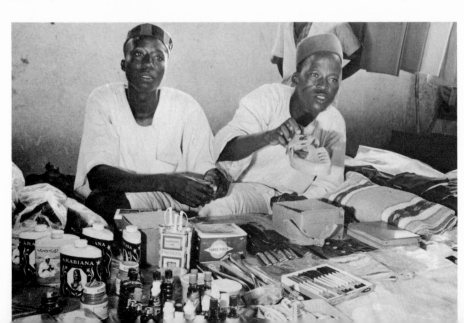

a change instead of a black one. I also buy a small white rubber ball for my little cousin Kwao. John and his brother sell all kinds of things: they sell shoes and locks and ink and cosmetics, towels and combs and spoons and ointments, string and matches and blankets and many more things.

John is from Nigeria. There are a few Nigerians who live in our village. They seem to like it here. I can recognize them by their clothes. They wear round caps and often have on multi-colored trousers. Esi the charcoal-seller is from Nigeria too. She wears a blouse with wide sleeves and a big turban on her head.

"I will read you the letter to the telephone people later, Kodjo—right after I type it," Kofi Appiah calls to me. "I will make a copy for Nana too!"

40

Behind John's and Edward's stall is a courtyard. There Bekoe the bronze-caster has his workshop. He is casting little figures and masks and drummers and turtles with snails and guns on their backs.

"Bekoe, could you cast a porcupine for me?" I ask.

41

"Of course I could cast a porcupine for you, but why do you want a porcupine? When did you become a tourist, Kodjo?" he asks. "You know we cast all these masks and animals and people for the foreigners who visit our country—it's a nice souvenir to remind them of their trip to Africa. It brings in good money too. What do you want it for?"

"I think if I had a bronze porcupine in my room I would be lucky and catch a live one again," I say. "I want to have one again. I miss my porcupine. I left it in Tamale. Every day I fed it on leftover cassava roots. It got so used to me that it wouldn't let anyone else near it. When my brothers or sisters tried to feed it, it got angry and started thrashing its tail! I named it Gyaeme—Leave Me Alone! I guess my family has made a meal out of it since I left. That makes me sad. They should have set it free again."

"I will make you one of bronze, Kodjo—as soon as I finish casting these figures in my oven. It shall bring you luck. But now I'd better blow the fire up again with my bellows."

"*Medase!*" I say. "Thank you. Would you like some white clay in return for making me the porcupine?"

"Do I look ill?" Bekoe calls out, surprised. "I do not have a fever! I do not have bites! I do not have the devil in me either! So why do you want to bring me white clay?"

"I thought I would bring you white clay to repair your oven, Bekoe. It looks cracked to me. I know a new place in the bush where I can get it." We use white clay for insect bites, and when we have a fever we smear it over our bodies to bring the fever down.

"Thank you, that is a good idea. Listen to that screaming! It's the vultures again. I really don't like them!"

"Look! Look! There is a big one diving toward Yaa! It is pecking away at the popcorn on her head. What a fresh one!" I call out.

We really laugh. The vulture circles over Yaa's head and then he dives all the way down and sits for a minute on the large plate on her head filled with nuts and corn. Now he takes a beakful and makes off, joining the other vultures that sit up on the roof.

Yaa juggles her plate around—the vulture almost upset it, but still she manages to keep it on her head.

"They are not getting any of *my* sweets!" shouts little Kwao and hides them in his hands under his cloth. "Those robbers!"

"I thought he wanted to grab my cross," Kwami shouts. "His feathers brushed my face!"

"Maybe he wanted to carry you up to the roof by the string of your cross!" I shout to Kwami. "It would be funny to see you standing up there with all the vultures!"

44

"Those birds could eat you up!" Akoskia says to little Kwao. "I saw them eating a dead bush pig!"

"Vultures don't eat living people!" Duah calls over. "Don't you frighten Kwao." Duah often walks through the village with his big trumpet, playing all kinds of tunes. He is always practicing for church festivals. The neighbors throw him out when he practices at home too much, so he walks through the village playing his songs. We all like to listen, and people sometimes start dancing or singing to his tunes.

45

Just now, Duah is playing a tune I know. It is to a poem by Kobina Parkes who lives in Accra, the capital of Ghana. Charlotte, who is selling spices for cooking and herbs for healing, has a good, loud voice. Duah plays and we all crowd around when she starts singing:

> Give me black souls,
> Let them be black
> Or chocolate brown
> Or make them the color
> of dust—
> Dustlike,
> Browner than sand.
> But if you can
> Please keep them black,
> Black!

"I can't sing very well lately—this baby in my belly takes all my breath away!" Charlotte complains. "But when the little rascal is born, he will be crying his head off—he'd better learn to sing right away. I am teaching him now and I hope he is listening!"

Duah walks on, playing a jazz tune, and Charlotte begins to call out her herbs and spices again. She really has everything to take care of colds and aches and dizziness and insect bites. She had a special herb for my stomach cramps a few days ago when I ate a rotten egg. The cramps disappeared—only her medicine tasted even worse than the rotten egg.

But when people have a serious illness they send for the doctor from the infirmary or they walk over themselves. The doctor and the nurse have many modern medicines and they give us injections when we get bitten by a snake or when we have a high temperature.

I run home and change into my shorts and shirt again, because I am going to work.

Our courtyard is very quiet. Everybody except Great-grand-mother has gone to the bush to harvest cocoa pods. Even my bush knife is gone! I stuff an orange into my pocket and run toward the bush.

There is a narrow footpath that leads to our cocoa trees. Through the trees I can see my family working—all except Nana who is at the cocoa-marketing board in the village. He sees to it that every farmer gets fair treatment and isn't cheated on the scales.

All around me the cocoa pods hang heavy on the trees. They are now orange-gold in color, which means they are ripe and ready to be cut. Before they ripen, the pods are green.

Uncle Frederick, who sometimes takes me hunting, told me that the best cocoa comes from this part of Ghana. That is because the cocoa trees are all protected from the sun and wind by larger trees that grow around them, and because the cocoa farmers take very good care of their trees—they look after them constantly. If they see black spots on the pods they immediately destroy the beans because the spots mean

they have a disease that may spread to other trees.

We cut the orange-gold pods from the tree with the slash of a very sharp bush knife. We do it very carefully so we do not cut into the tree itself and bruise it. Uncle Frederick has showed me time and again how to slash off the pods. I practiced on a tree that had "swollen shoot" disease, which kills the whole tree anyway. "Swollen shoot" is a virus, and you can not see it because it is so very small. It is carried from tree to tree by little insects. When those insects feed on an infected tree they pick up the virus and carry it around.

"I took your knife, Kodjo!" calls Annan, when he sees me. "The blacksmith promised me a new blade yesterday—remember? I broke mine when I was repairing Bekoe's old motorcycle. I guess I shouldn't have used it as a screwdriver! He doesn't have it ready yet. I am sure it will be finished when the harvest is over."

Annan is my cousin and he can use my bush knife whenever he wants to. He always puts it back under my bed.

"I am going over to help with the plantain leaves anyway—you can keep it until I need it!"

First you'd better help with opening the pods, Kodjo," Uncle Frederick calls to me. "Did you forget they have to be opened as soon as possible after they are cut, so they will dry out? We do not have enough people around today to open the pods, because so many of the women are busy cooking and preparing for Nana Sabranu's arrival. We can use two more hands around here. Use my short knife for slashing them open—it is faster with a short knife anyway. Then Annan can continue cutting the pods with your long knife."

I sit down and start to open the pods to take out the white beans.

"If we are short-handed, why aren't you working with the cocoa too?" I ask Uncle Frederick. "You are digging out yams instead."

"Silly boy!" Uncle Frederick calls out with a laugh. "This big yam root was interfering with one of our best cocoa trees. It was growing right next to the tree trunk instead of on my field, and it took the water away from the roots of the cocoa tree. So I pulled it out.

50

We will have some nice *fufu* from this big yam root tonight—with garden-eggs and onions and pepper soup! And we will drink a lot of palmwine with it!

"Listen to the *atumpan*—the talking drum! It is telling everybody about Nana Sabranu's visit this afternoon. The drum just said, 'A

very important guest is coming! A very important guest is coming!' Didn't you hear it?"

"I think what you are hearing is Uncle Kivashie's portable radio!" I say. "He carries it with him even to the bush! You know that they use drum beats now as an interval signal on the radio. Yesterday I saw Uncle Kivashie sitting in front of his hut ironing shirts and listening to the children's program on Radio Ghana. He said he learns a lot from children's programs. I wish we had a radio too. They told the story about Tetteh Quarshie, the blacksmith who brought the first cocoa beans over from Fernando Po."

"I learned about Tetteh from Great-grandfather," Uncle Frederick says. "He was a blacksmith in Great-grandpa's village. That was about eighty years ago, I think. Great-grandpa said Tetteh had a handful of strange brown seeds in his pocket, which he had gathered from some short trees on an island called Fernando Po. He thought those seeds would bring him more money than being a blacksmith ever would. And he certainly was right!

"Tetteh planted the seeds, and tended the young plants very carefully. He planted banana and cassava trees right next to them for shade. And five years later came the first of the crop that made our country known throughout the whole world: cocoa! Some of Tetteh's trees are still growing near the village."

52

"They said in the papers yesterday that Ghana now supplies more than two-thirds of all the cocoa in the world! Over a millon people grow cocoa trees in our country," I tell Uncle Frederick.

"It all started a few years after Tetteh Quarshie's death," Uncle Frederick continues. "Cocoa-growing spread over the southern part of our country—and it brought good money to his family and to thousands of villagers. Our money grows on cocoa trees really!"

53

"If you are going to stand around like that chatting, chatting, chatting, the money on our trees will rot away!" Aunt Lucretia calls over. "I thought you could do two things at the same time, Kodjo.

"See that big pile over there? All those pods must be split open today," my aunt says. "Split them carefully, so you don't damage the beans inside!" As if I did not know.

Now Aunt Lucretia is acting exactly like Mother—always telling me how to do things.

Some of the women sitting next to me crack the pod with a stick instead of with a knife. Aunt Lucretia is an expert at that. She splits the pods with two or three sharp blows.

I scrape out the white beans and the sticky pulp around them. Then I place the beans on large plantain leaves and cover them with more leaves. They will ferment between the leaves for six days, and every other day we will come and mix them so they ferment evenly. They turn all brown after they have fermented. Only then do we place the beans on mats in the village and expose them to the sunlight to dry them completely.

When a cocoa bean is still white it tastes very bitter, but when it is brown it tastes and smells like chocolate. That is why we ferment the beans—to get the cocoa flavor.

"Can we help too?" Kwasi and Kobina shout over from the bush trail to Aunt Lucretia. "Can we cut off some pods?" As usual Kwasi is carrying his big bush knife with him. I hardly ever see him without it.

"You can cut some more plantain leaves to cover the beans," Aunt Lucretia tells them. "And only cut very big leaves!"

"I saw a porcupine on the way here," Kwasi tells me. "I know you want one, but l was afraid to catch it. All I could see were a lot of quills. It rattled them very noisily and looked as if it wanted to attack me. Kobina started to run after it, but I held him back. Porcupines are dangerous, aren't they?"

"They are, but you can tame them once you catch them and they get to know you," I say.

"I am sure you will catch one soon," Aunt Lucretia says to me. "You won't be happy till you have a porcupine. Ask Uncle Frederick to go after one with you. Just don't plan to keep it in our courtyard— it's too crowded already with our big family! But there will always be plenty for it to eat."

We work away. It is very hot in the bush, and very sticky. No wind blows here at all. It is much worse than in our classroom. The heat and the humidity are good for the cocoa trees, but I am not a cocoa tree and I don't like it at all.

At last we are finished. The beans are covered with plantain leaves and the place is covered with broken shells and the soft white sticky pulp.

We walk home on the bush trail in single file, carrying big baskets full of cocoa beans on our heads. These are the beans we wrapped in plantain leaves five days ago. They have fermented already. Luckily the cocoa does not all ripen at exactly the same time. We would not be able to cut all the pods off so quickly.

"*God's Gift* is coming! *God's Gift* is coming!" I hear Tettey shouting from the highroad. He doesn't want anyone to miss the bus. But today not many people are going to the bus stop. They want to stay in the village to see the chiefs.

"All our buses should look like that!" Tettey goes on shouting. He often shouts out his opinions on things and wants everybody to listen to him. "We live in modern times!" he goes on. "I don't like buses like *The Last Ride* and *Don't Argue with Me* any more. I will only ride on the new Mammy lorries from now on! Let the old ones go out of business!"

"You are right!" many people shout back to Tettey.

Tettey is the only one in the village who works with an umbrella in the sun. "I am just like a cocoa bean," he told everybody. "One has to be careful about exposing beans to the sun, otherwise they burn—and so do I." Yesterday he asked everybody who passed him, "What is the difference between a cocoa bean and myself?" Nobody

knew the answer, and then Tettey said, "The only difference between a cocoa bean and myself is that the cocoa bean was born white and I was born black." And then he laughed at his joke.

We empty our baskets in front of Tettey on large tables and spread the brown cocoa beans evenly. Tettey and his sister and brother turn and rub the beans every day and make sure each one is thoroughly dry. He is in charge of the cocoa beans for our family. Every night Tettey covers the beans against rain or dew. They

must not get wet. And every day we look for bad beans—whenever someone in our family passes our tables—and then we just throw them away.

The bad ones are moldy or flat, and some even have insects in them. It's very important that we find all the faulty beans, Uncle Frederick explained to me, because later when the beans are completely dry, they are brought to the cocoa-marketing board. There, people grade them. If they find that more than five percent of the beans are bad, they are labeled "grade two," but if less than five percent of the beans are bad, then they get a "grade one" label, and we get a much better price for them. I often go with Uncle Frederick to the marketing board to see how the agent there works. He picks a hundred beans and cuts them in half. Then he puts a half of each in a frame which is divided into one hundred little squares. He counts the faulty beans and that is how he figures the percentage.

57

I run home, take off my shirt, go to the kitchen, and start pounding the yam into *fufu* with a long stick.

My cousin Kwami helps me with it. He turns the yam around quickly with his hands just before I hit it with the stick.

58

"That is what I like to see!" Aunt Lucretia says when she enters the yard. "It is nice to have a nephew around! But you can stop pounding now, Kodjo, Kwaku will take over, and I will turn the yam." I give the stick to him gladly. "Ah! What a good harvest this has been!" my aunt calls over to her mother and to her grandmother who are sitting on the steps outside their rooms. "See this basket of beans? Not a single bad bean

among them, I am sure! Nana won't mind spending some money on pretty cloth for us, eh? After all, he gets more money for his cocoa beans when they are all healthy."

I walk over to the blackboard and start making a chalk drawing.

"*I* am using the blackboard now," Kwabla says. "I have to practice my arithmetic!" Kwabla is my second youngest cousin—he is the best of our whole family in school. He is even good at spelling!

"Just move over a bit," I say. "We can *both* use the blackboard."

There is hardly any chalk left but I am used to that. Annan and Felicia and Kwami use the chalk constantly for homework. But more often they just scribble with it, and then it gets broken. I run into my room and get a new piece of chalk out of my chalkbox. Nobody knows about it because I keep it hidden under my pillow.

"Kodjo, what are you drawing?" Ajete asks me through the window.

"I know what it is—trails through the bush!" Kwami calls. "Can you put palm trees in your picture too?"

60

"I think it looks like a lot of snakes!" Kwabla shouts.

"Kodjo is painting his brain," Kwaku calls to me. "My mother once fried the brain of one of our goats for a meal—it looked exactly like that!"

"Could you all please disappear!" I shout. "Or else I will chase you into the bush! Listen—it's the bells of the hair-coloring man! Run and line up or you won't get your hair blackened in time!"

They all run away at last. It's a good thing that Dade the hair-coloring man came. He stops right in front of our house.

"I had my hair blackened yesterday," Kwabla says. He is still doing his arithmetic.

"I did too," I say. Nana asked Dade to come over to our yard so we wouldn't have to wait in line for a long time.

Dade goes through the village with a bottle of black dye and rubber gloves and a big brush. He uses the same dye on our hair as Francis uses on the *adinkra* cloth when he prints his designs.

We only have our hair dyed for special occasions, such as the deer-hunting festival or the drumming competition at Christmas time or the yam-harvest festival or the cocoa-harvest festival. Then we all like to look more beautiful, and Dade and the other hair-dressers have a lot to do.

Today, head chief Nana Sabranu is coming, and many other Nanas too, so we all want to look our best.

"Don't pull too hard!" I hear Aunt Stella call angrily to a friend who is doing her hair. "Please twist it slowly!" Aunt Stella often grumbles.

"I have to pull hard if you want to look beautiful for the chiefs!"

"This black dye does two things at the same time," I hear Dade say to Kofi. It cleans your hair *and* makes it more beautiful. Right?"

"And I like the smell of the dye!" little Kofi says. "It smells of a sweet I like to eat."

"Don't you ever taste this dye!" Dade warns Kofi. "You would get cramps. It's only for dyeing hair and cloth!"

"Couldn't you dye Buruburu and Wiwi black?" Kofi asks. "They would look nice. I think they would like it."

"Buruburu and Wiwi can not pay me—and I do not want customers who can not pay!" Dade says and laughs. "You see, your mother pays me for doing your hair!"

Buruburu and Wiwi are Uncle Frederick's hunting dogs. He named them after two big streams in our country because they both swim so well. He told me they once even chased a crocodile, but the crocodile swam too fast and they couldn't catch it.

Up north, where I lived before, we believe that half of our soul lives inside the crocodile, and so we never kill one.

"Kodjo, come on, let's play *oware!*" my friend Francis calls. "I have plenty of ababo beans. The chiefs are not on the road yet. Kwami and Kwaku went to the bridge—they will call us when they see them. We won't miss them!"

"You still owe me a game," Uncle Aduad tells me. "Remember you beat me last time we played?"

"I remember," I say, "and I hope to do it again!"

"You do! Well let's just see!"

We sit down on our stools in the yard and I bring out the *oware* board and my ababo beans. Each player puts beans into each of the six holes on the board. We play by grabbing a bean and passing it from one hole to another very quickly.

If a player can add a fourth bean to those in any of his opponent's holes he captures them. And whoever has the most beans at the end of the game wins! One has to be quick with one's hand and I like to play it for hours and hours.

"Adaud is winning everything back from you, Kodjo!" says Great-

grandfather from the window. "Don't despair—I have often lost all my ababo beans! I played many a game when I was your age. Ah, but that was a very long time ago—probably a hundred years. It was the time of Osei Kwaku Dua I. He was my good friend and a great *Asantehene*! It was during the time we had big battles with the British. Sometimes *they* won the battles and sometimes *we* won! We suffered greatly: many of our villages were burned down by them and we were forced to abandon our farms. The British suffered too—they often became very ill, because they were not used to our hot, humid climate. They even got sick from the food. Many, many soldiers died.

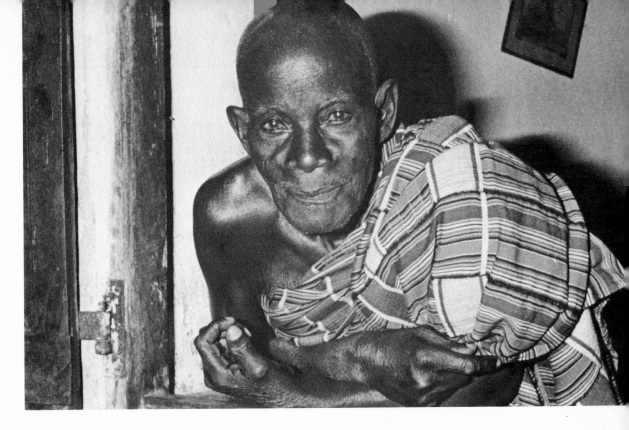

"At that time too, the whole Gold Coast was hit by terrible earthquakes. Even the big castles and forts of the British at the coast were damaged. Ah, but all that happened long, long ago!

"And why am I telling you all this? Just because I remembered my good friend who always beat me when we played *oware* together. Ah, but he has been dead a long, long time. I have outlived all my good friends! There are no more wars now in our country. The British are gone and we are free and independent. Ah, that I was allowed to see this!"

Great-grandfather is over a hundred years old, but he still has very good eyes and ears—only his legs are weak and he often has to be carried around when he wants to visit someone.

Great-grandfather could really be a history teacher. He remembers so many stories from more than a hundred years ago, and he knew all the great chiefs of our tribe. He himself is the son of a chief. And he loves to talk. You only have to ask him one question and then you get a whole history lesson as an answer! We often crowd around him in the evening and listen to his stories.

65

"The drums!" Kwami and Kwaku come running from the bridge shouting to us. "The drums! They are coming! Great Nana Sabranu is coming!" We stop playing at once.

"Will you carry me over to the bench near the road, Kodjo?" Great-grandfather asks.

"I will Great-grandpa! Just let me put on my *kente*!" Everybody is running to the road to meet the chiefs. The talking drums come closer—they say "Very important guests are arriving! Come to greet them!"

Uncle Aduad and I carry Great-grandfather to the road and sit him down on a chair not far from my uncle, our village's Nana. He is welcoming all the chiefs from the other villages and offering them seats. He asks them how they are and whether their villages are prospering, and telling them that he hopes they are having a good cocoa harvest this year! Each one has on his most beautiful *kente*, the national cloth, today.

Right next to Nana sits his *okyeame*, his speaker, holding the golden staff with the chameleon on top. When Nana wants to make a speech, he never speaks himself—he always whispers the words to his *okyeame* and lets him speak. One can easily recognize an *okyeame*, because he always has a long golden speaker's staff in his hand.

When I came to live with his family, I asked Nana why there was a chameleon on top of the golden staff. He told me that he is known to the people for being flexible, for sometimes changing his opinion as the chameleon changes his colors. And so the people decided he should have a chameleon on the speaker's staff. The chief who visited Nana last week with his *okyeame* had a golden staff with a hand holding an egg on top of his staff. Nana explained later what it meant. He said, "To be a ruler is like holding an egg in your hand. If it is held too tightly it breaks, but if it is not held tightly enough it may slip and smash on the ground. It is difficult to find the golden middle path. Remember this saying," Nana told

me. "One day you will succeed me and I hope you will be a wise and good Nana—and that you will listen to your good friends when they give you advice and not just push your own ideas through. Be firm *and* gentle and try to help your people." I get very excited when I think that one day I will be Nana! I will raise money to install electric lights and I will open an art school here one day too!

The big drums are pounding noisily in front of Nana Sabranu. Two enormous umbrellas are held above the *denkyedenkye*, the long basket in which the chief is carried around.

The umbrellas dance wildly—the bearers are pushing them up and down so that the chief will get a breeze from them. Our whole village is assembling near the road. The rhythm of the drumbeat affects many people. They begin to sing and dance around the *denkyedenkye*, welcoming the chief. We are all very happy that he has come to our village—it is a great honor.

"The chiefs are going to dicuss whether we have collected enough money to build a big new school house," Uncle Aduad explains to

me. "Yes, I know—I think we have," I say. "Everybody went to the community hall a few Sundays ago with donations, don't you remember?"

"A big modern school costs a lot of money, Kodjo—the donations may not be enough—although the government will give us half the money for the school," Uncle Aduad says. "We will see."

"But if the cocoa harvest is such a good one this year, the people can give more money for the school!" I say.

"Not everybody likes to spend money on a community project," Uncle Aduad says. "Our family does, but many people have to be told over and over to give for others. That is why we assembled the chiefs of many villages here today. They will speak to us through their speakers and after hearing their words, the people will give more money I am sure. Your uncle has prepared a good speech too! After his last speech people gave a lot of money for the new road through the bush. A good speech often brings a lot of money!"

"*Akwaaba! Akwaaba!*" everybody shouts now and claps his
hands as Nana Sabranu comes near. "Welcome! Welcome!" He is
doing a sword dance with his arms on his *denkyedenkye*. The four
people who carry him rock him back and forth to the rhythm of
the drumbeat. On both sides of Nana Sabranu walk the sword-
bearers. Kwabla, my friend who sanded our new *oware* game, is
among them.

"Did you catch your porcupine
yet?" Kwabla calls over to me.
Nana Sabranu hears him and
looks surprised. "No, not yet—
but I will!" I call back. "Maybe
I will catch one tonight!"

70

Nana Sabranu stops dancing and calls to me, "The bush is full of porcupines this year! What do you want one for?" I draw back with surprise and I am ashamed for talking to a swordbearer. But Nana Sabranu winks at me and laughs! "I will make a cage for it and keep it there and feed it." I say reverently. "Porcupines love to roam around free," Nana Sabranu calls back, and he orders his bearers to stop for a moment. Everybody listens now. "Animals love freedom, just as every human being loves freedom! You wouldn't want to be kept in a cage and fed nicely, would you? Let's not dominate the animals. Let them be as free as we are. Let them lead *their* way of life, or they won't be happy. Not all animals like to be pets. They may even die in captivity! Catch a tortoise instead— and give it a big place to live in!"

My friends all look at me, because Nana Sabranu has spoken so many words to me.

71

The procession moves on. But I slowly walk home. I am very excited. Nana Sabranu's words have made me sad, because he meant I should not keep a porcupine. Maybe he is right and I should not have a porcupine as a pet. Maybe I made my last porcupine unhappy when I kept it in a cage. Nana Sabranu is a very wise man. I only kept the porcupine to have a pet to play with, but it may not even have wanted to play with me. The trouble is that animals can not talk. It would be much easier if they could. I would have asked my porcupine.

I enter the yard. Only Great-grandmother sits in her usual place on the steps. Everybody else is away. I think she is asleep. I pass her quickly and go into my room. I do not want to talk to anybody now. I take my *kente* off, fold it neatly, and lie on the bed to think. I don't mind that I will not hear the speeches and I don't mind that I will not see all the other chiefs—Nana Sabranu was right. I will not catch a porcupine. I will let it run around free in the bush.

Maybe I will catch a tortoise one day, or I will ask Uncle Frederick to give me a puppy the next time Buruburu has little ones.

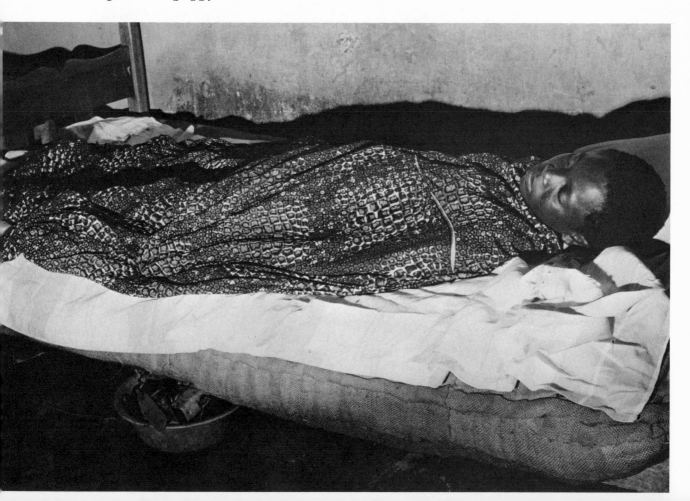

From far away I hear the boom of the drums and the shrill cry of the birds. Through the open door I see the setting sun. It is a glowing red ball today. Another minute and it will be gone.

Bekoe promised to cast a bronze porcupine for me. I will keep it to remind me of my old pet.

Glossary

Ababo   A type of tree

Accra   The capital of Ghana

Adinkra   A series of designs

Akwaaba!   Welcome!

Asantehene   Paramount chief

Atumpan   Drum

Badi   A type of tree

Bra!   Come here!

Calabash   A round green fruit from which utensils and jars
are made

Cassava   A cabbage-like plant with starchy roots

Denkyedenkye   A sedan chair

Durbar   A festival of the Ashanti region

Fufu   A paste made of vegetables

Kenke   Mashed corn wrapped in palm leaves

Kente   The national cloth of Ghana, worn on festive
occasions

Kumasi   The capital of the Ashanti region

Kuntinkantan   A series of designs

Kwaku Ananse   A clever spider; a central figure in Ashanti folklore

Kwasu   Fool

Medase!   Thank you!

Nana   Chief of a village

Ntoma   A cloth worn during leisure time

Okyeame   Spokesman for a chief

Oware   A game played with seeds, beans, or marbles

Tu mirika!   Run on!

Postscript

The Republic of Ghana, shaped roughly like a rectangle, lies just north of the equator in West Africa and shares common boundaries with Upper Volta in the north, Ivory Coast in the west, and Togo in the east.

Ghana's 92,000 square miles vary from forest and bush on the coastal plain to open savanna (or grassland) with few trees in the north. Ghana's climate is tropical and there are two rainy seasons around May and September.

Like most African countries, Ghana was a European colony for many years. A profitable traffic in gold and slaves led to exploitation of the country by foreign traders. In fact, so much gold was obtained that the country came to be known as the Gold Coast. In 1807, British parliament declared the slave trade illegal and shortly afterward began the Ashanti wars which marked the course of the greater part of the nineteenth century. In 1874 the British annexed the coastal region which then was officially named the Gold Coast Colony, but not until 1901 was peace restored to the area with the annexation of the Ashanti Empire.

On March 6, 1957, the Gold Coast became an independent state and was renamed Ghana after an ancient Sudanic Empire. It was the first British colony in Africa to achieve independence.

Although the official language is English, the almost eight million people of Ghana speak more than fifty local languages and dialects. The predominant religions are Christianity and Islam, along with a number of tribal religions.

Ghana is a richly endowed country. It is the world's largest producer of cocoa, and also exports gold, diamonds, manganese, and timber.

Ghana's flag shows three horizontal stripes. A red stripe honors those Ghanians who worked for its independence. A green stripe stands for the country's forests and farms. A gold stripe tells of its mineral wealth. In this middle stripe of gold, a black star proclaims its proud black people's independence and freedom.

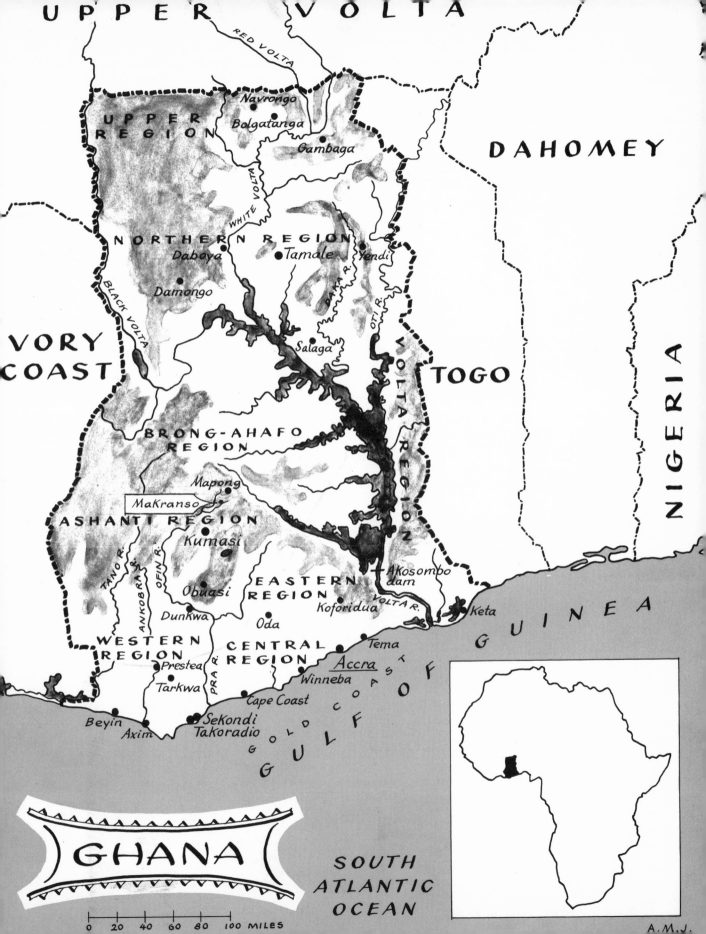